BELAIR LESSON BANK

Themes for Poetry

Fred Sedgwick

Contents

Acknowledgements

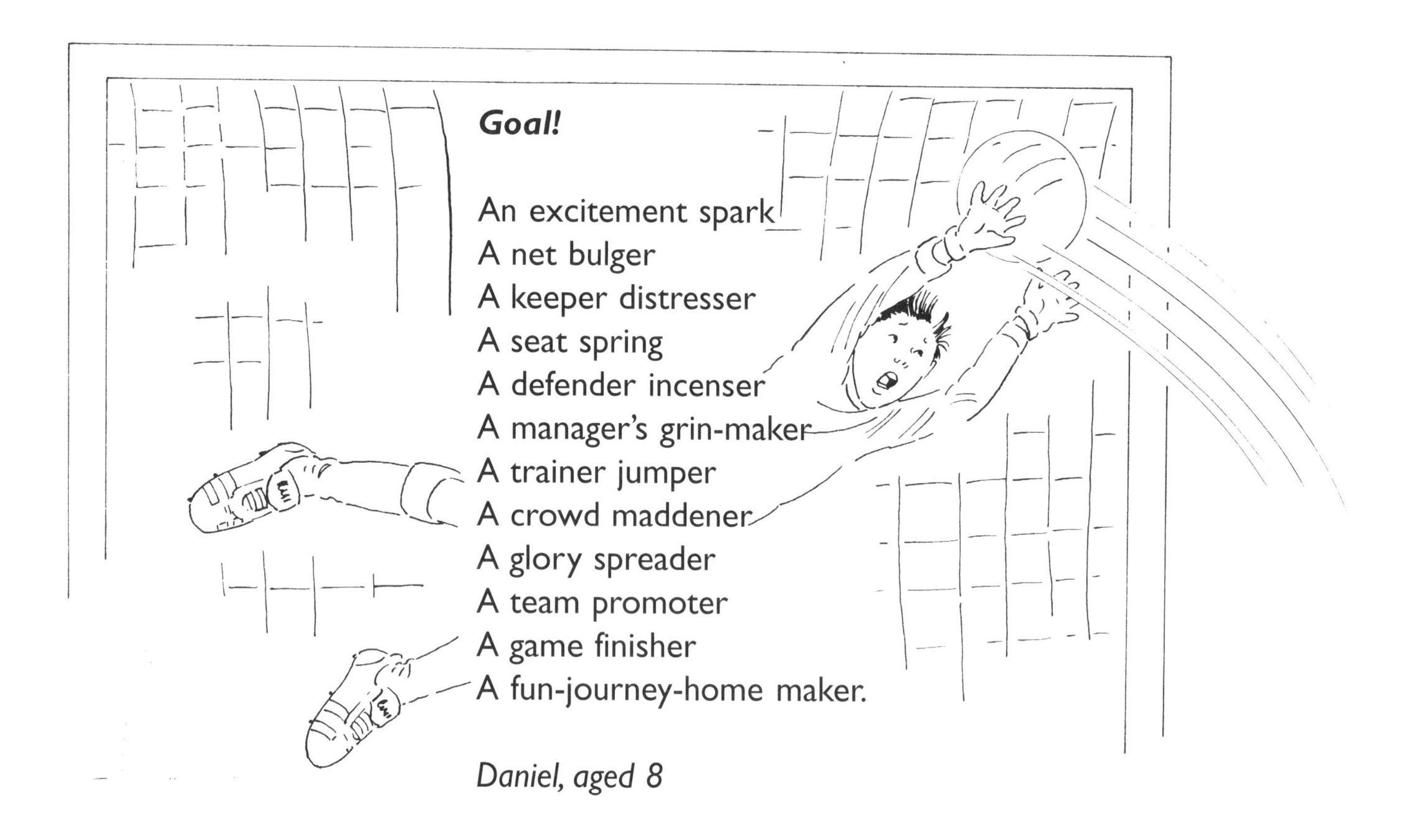

Goal!

An excitement spark
A net bulger
A keeper distresser
A seat spring
A defender incenser
A manager's grin-maker
A trainer jumper
A crowd maddener
A glory spreader
A team promoter
A game finisher
A fun-journey-home maker.

Daniel, aged 8

First published 2000 by Belair Publications.
United Kingdom: Belair Publications, Albert House, Apex Business Centre, Boscombe Road, Dunstable, LU5 4RL.

The author wishes to thank the staff and pupils of: Nascot Wood Junior School, Watford, Hertfordshire; St Laurence's RCVAP School, Cambridge, especially Christopher Wardle and headteacher Brigida Martino; and Little Bealings School, Ipswich, especially headteacher Duncan Bathgate.

Editor: Terry Vittachi
Layout artist: Suzanne Ward
Cover design: Martin Cross
Illustrations: Liz McIntosh, Linda Rogers Associates

Every effort has been made to contact copyright holders of material used in this book. If any have been overlooked, we will be pleased to make any necessary arrangements.

British Library Cataloguing in Publication Data. A catalogue record for this book is available from the British Library.

Fred Sedgwick hereby asserts his moral right to be identified as the author of this work in accordance with the Copyright, Designs and Patents Act 1988.

ISBN 1 84191 046–5

Introduction

Themes for Poetry (for ages 7–9) is one of a series of books designed to help children enjoy poetry while they learn about its many forms. Poetry is arguably unique in its ability to stretch and challenge children because, by its very nature, it differs from the prose fiction and non-fiction which forms the bulk of their reading; it introduces children to new, exciting, dynamic forms of creativity and self-expression, using a wide variety of poetic devices from traditional rhyme to free verse. The series aims to stimulate a lifelong interest in and appreciation of poetry, encourage children to compose their own poems, and motivate them to seek out new favourite writers of their own, extending their reading and developing a new perspective on their relationship with language. Many of the poems featured in the books are written by children, letting your class see what children are capable of and inspiring them to similar heights.

The structure of the book

Themes for Poetry explores new ways of using everyday themes to help children learn to appreciate poetry and stimulate them to write poems of their own.

Each chapter is designed to give ideas for class, group and individual work, following a similar pattern. The poetry sheet features one or more poems, which can be photocopied. Ideally you will introduce the poem, and either you or one or more of the children will read it aloud. This could be followed by some initial discussion exploring how each poem achieves its effect, and encouraging the children to develop their own thoughts for the theme.

The children can then move on to the activity sheets, either in groups or individually. The activities allow the children to think about the theme, experiment and play with words, and brainstorm their ideas. Sometimes the children are asked to write their own poems; further suggestions for written work are also given.

Poetic devices

As well as encouraging children to enjoy poetry, the book also introduces them to different poetic devices to enrich both their reading and their writing. *Themes for Poetry* covers metaphor, simile, alliteration, onomatopoeia, synonyms, haiku and kennings, and you might find it helpful to have a selection of samples of each of these to use during the appropriate lesson.

General principles

- Offer your own ideas, but make sure you lay claim to them. Say something like 'You can't use that, because I thought of it, but I'm sure you can think of something even better.'

- Handwriting, spelling and grammar are not vital at the stage when the children are making their notes. This is the 'first draft' stage, where the main objective is for the children to get their ideas down into note form which they can read. They will be buzzing with ideas, and you do not want to impede their creativity. When the final version is made, you can attend to the technical aspects.

- The five senses are vital to vivid poetry. 'What can you hear/smell/see/touch/taste?' are always useful questions.

- You and the children should play with the poems: recite them in different ways, and have fun with them.

Belair Lesson Banks on CD

All Belair *Lesson Banks* come in a CD format as well as book format. The CDs offer the children the opportunity to work on a computer, a learning tool they often find stimulating, while working through the same high quality activities found in the book.

Key features

- The discs have many different activities on them including responding to pictures, writing frames, working in tables, sorting and matching activities, and scored 'multi-choice' questions.
- Many of the activities can be altered. If you, as the teacher, want to modify the language or change a question, you can do so easily. You can make changes such as:
  - simplify the text
  - add complexity to the language and structure
  - provide model answers or examples.
- Many screens have a linked screen which gives the children an opportunity to write an extended piece in response to a question. The linked screen will automatically print out with the original screen.
- Finally, you can of course modify the activities on screen and print them out for the children to use as paper activities.

ideas page

Observation and the senses

Introduction

For this exercise, ask the children to bring in a stone and a piece of grass, a leaf, some bark, clover or a rosehip. You will be asking the class to examine these objects with all of their senses, then to describe their findings using metaphors and similes to aid their descriptions. The children will then use this experience to compose their own poem.

Learning Objectives

- To understand and use metaphors and similes.
- To compare different views of the same subject using the five senses.
- To compose poems based on close observation of natural objects.

Discussion

- Begin by holding up your own stone. Have some comparisons ready to help you describe it to the class; for example, it may look like an egg, or a potato, or a planet. Then ask the children to hold their stones, close their eyes, and feel the stone carefully in different ways. How does it feel when they clutch it? Stroke it? Graze their knuckles against it? Ask them how many ways of touching the stone they can think of. A few minutes of this will contribute to the quality of the children's observation.
- Next ask the class to look at their stones. Ask them to describe the stones' surface patterns, colours and shapes. Encourage the children to produce similes using the word 'as', and to compose metaphors by beginning sentences with 'The stone is like ...'
- Write some of their similes and metaphors on the board, focusing on the most original.
- Suggest to the children that very close observation of the world around them can help them to understand and enjoy it more. Looking at stones, flowers and trees 'until it hurts', as William Blake says, can be an enriching experience. Suggest that they choose one thing to look at very hard each day.

Activity Pages

All about stones

Divide the class into groups and ask the children to read the poem *Stone* on the poetry page, silently and to themselves. Then ask the groups to discuss their stones, comparing them with each other's. Encourage them to use a thesaurus to find appropriate words to describe colours and textures. Give the children five minutes to write down, as quickly as they can, any words or ideas they have in their heads about stones. This is best done in silence. The activity page also asks the children to make drawings of their stone; this will enrich their observation and their writing. When the children draw their pictures, encourage them to use their pencils in a variety of ways so that they capture the shading and shape of their stone.

The grass is like a field of spears

Do the same for the grasses or leaves the children have brought in. Have a store of different grasses ready for children who have not brought in anything.

Written Work

- Ask the children to use their notes to:
  - write a short poem about a stone
  - write a short poem about grass
  - write a short poem about any other natural object.
- Invite the class to look at a patch of sky (with appropriate safety warnings about not staring at the sun), and ask them to write a poem about the particular patch they have been staring at.
- Ask the children to look at some of the following manufactured objects in the same way, and to write observational poems about them:
  - bicycle
  - car engine
  - PE equipment
  - light bulb

Observation and the senses

Poetry page

Stone

It's a cool weight
in the palm of my hand.

It smells of pink earthworms coiled
on rainy mornings.

Hurled through the air,
it would hurt me badly.

If I tasted it,
it would taste of earth.

That wouldn't be so bad perhaps:
to taste the earth.

Fred Sedgwick

Rosehip

It looks like fire swaying.
If I tasted it, it would taste like the sun, burning hot.
In my body it would be like a muscle, gleaming red.
In the summer, is it going to be a rose?

Eleanor, aged 8

Apple

There is a red and green apple which is dirty.
The top is like a tree that has been chopped down.
When you sliced it, it fell apart.
The pip is shaped like half a pear or a raindrop.
The inside of the apple looks like cartoon eyes.

Max, aged 9

All about stones

Read *Stone* on the poetry page.

Look at your own stone and describe it in the space below. Think of two different endings for the same beginning. (If your stone is rough, think of two rough words, such as 'It feels as rough as sandpaper'.)

Example: It feels as smooth as an **egg**.

1. It feels as ____________________ .

2. It feels as ____________________ .

Example: It feels as hard as a **cricket ball**.

1. It feels as ____________________ .

2. It feels as ____________________ .

Suggest two things that it nearly looks like – use your imagination!

Example: It looks like **an old potato**.

1. It looks like ____________________ .

2. It looks like ____________________ .

NOW

Draw a picture of your stone in the space below. Look for patterns and colours and shapes on the stone. Around your drawing write some words that describe the feel and look of it.

The grass is like a field of spears

Read *Rosehip* and *Apple* on the poetry page. What does your grass remind you of? Is it like a spear? A knife? Draw and label three things that your blade of grass is like.

1. Now find **one** of these:

a clover leaf	a piece of bark	a fragment of sky (you will have to look at this from a distance)
a leaf from a tree	a rosehip	

On a separate sheet make a careful drawing of whatever you have chosen. Keep looking at it while you draw.

2. Now smell your object. Write down two things that its smell reminds you of. One example is done for you.

My **piece of bark** smells like **damp earth after rain**.

____ .

____ .

3. Next use your imagination to describe two things that your object might taste like – but don't put it in your mouth!

Remember, don't really taste it!

My **piece of bark** might taste like **the air on Guy Fawkes' night**.

____ .

____ .

Write a poem about your object. Say what it looks like, what it smells like and what it might taste like.

ideas page

Space

Introduction

This exercise will improve the children's knowledge of the solar system and encourage them to incorporate that knowledge into the writing of short poems, particularly haiku. A haiku has exactly 17 syllables; some children (and adults) will find it challenging, so you may not want to be too rigid. The main objective is for the children to write short, vivid poems using the information they have found, rather than to focus too much on using exactly 17 syllables.

Learning Objectives

- To reinforce knowledge of the solar system.
- To learn about and compose short poems, particularly haiku.

Discussion

- If you are using this section, you are likely already to be working with your class on a project about space and the children will therefore have some knowledge of the solar system. Discuss the attributes of each planet (size, temperature and so on) and how these factors contribute to our perception of the planet's character. For example, Mercury is tiny and hot; Saturn is ringed; Mars is red; what do these qualities suggest? Explore with the children what they know about Earth and, using appropriate illustrations, what they might think about Earth if they were seeing it from the first time from outer space. Make extensive use of books, videos and CD ROMs; the more information you have available, the better.
- After the children have read the poems on the poetry page, have a class discussion. How does Eloise describe Venus? Can they find any descriptions of the planets used in the poems in the materials they have been looking at?
- Before asking the children to read the poems, it might be fun for them if you cover up the titles and see if they can guess which planet each poem is about.

Activity Pages

Finding out about planets

Have available a good selection of books, videos and CD ROMs about the solar system. Colour pictures are essential, as these will provide even more stimulation for the children's imagination. Ask the children to use these resources to help them prepare two or three paragraphs of information on a selected topic such as Mars or the Sun. When they have prepared the paragraphs, divide the class into groups of two or three and ask them to share their ideas. Then invite them to tell you their findings and collate their ideas in front of the whole class. They can then choose a different planet and begin the exercise.

Finding out about haiku

Make sure that the children are familiar with working out how many syllables there are in a word. Give some examples on the board. Use simple clapping games to help them distinguish between the syllables, with one clap per syllable, perhaps experimenting with the rhythm and pace of the sound.

The only other true haiku is 'Gold beak, jet feathers'.

Written Work

- Before they begin their haiku, ask the children to write a three-line poem about a planet of their choice, focusing on short, vivid imagery. Then they can write their haiku, being stricter about the traditional haiku form: five syllables in the first line, seven in the second and five in the third. Then ask the children to write a haiku about the moon or a star.
- Ask the class to think of single words or short phrases to describe the planet Saturn. Write their responses on the board. When you have collected enough words and phrases, ask the children to reproduce some of them on a sheet of paper, so as to make the shape of the planet Saturn, including its rings. This will give them a foretaste of working with shape poems, which are explored in more detail in *Forms of Poetry 1*, and will show them how to design patterns with words.

Space

Poetry page

Venus

Bauble of misty silver,
ferocious, violent under
a mask of beauty.

Eloise, aged 8

Earth

A big blue and green marble
spinning in the misty blackness,
staring at the star-studded sky.

Laura, aged 9

Mars

Red wrath of Mars, its
ruby red colour. The god of war lives in
his fiery planet.

Kashan, aged 9

Saturn

Lottery ball, rings
spinning in dark space, second
in the dark machine.

Ravi, aged 9

Pluto

The furthest away
is the little grey one
spinning on its own.

Laura, aged 7

Finding out about planets

1. Choose a planet. Find out as much as you can about it and fill in the table below.

What it is made of	Its main colours	What it looks like

2. Think about the size of the different planets. Write down three ways of describing the size of your planet.

Example: 'Jupiter is as big as an elephant.'

The planet ______________ is ______________________________________ .

The planet ______________ is ______________________________________ .

The planet ______________ is ______________________________________ .

3. Use the space below to write short notes about your planet. For example, you could write: 'Saturn. Spins fast. Thin rings around it. Has moons.'

Do the same for another planet in the solar system that you don't know much about. Then look it up in a book or on a CD ROM to see how right your guesses were.

Finding out about haiku

A haiku is a poem with exactly 17 syllables. Syllables are the sounds a word makes.

1. **Ravinder Singh** has four syllables.

Rav	in	der	Singh
1	2	3	4

Work out how many syllables there are in the name below. Split it up into its syllables, and write the number underneath. One has been done for you.

a) Jonathan MacAlister **b) Jenny Smith**

Jon	ath	an	Mac	A	lis	ter
1	2	3	4	5	6	7

Write your own name down. How many syllables does it have?

2. The 17 syllables of a haiku are usually (but not always) arranged like this:

5 in the first line	**7** in the second	**5** in the third

Look at these poems. Fill in the number of syllables in each line in the boxes. Then add them up to find the total number. Tick any that is a true haiku (with exactly 17 syllables arranged 5, 7, 5). The first one is done for you.

✔ Stars on a clear night. [5]
I gaze upwards, wondering, [7]
again, who made them. [5]
Total [17]

Gold beak, jet feathers. [ ]
He stands on my neighbour's bush: [ ]
fat, handsome blackbird. [ ]
Total [ ]

A winter morning. [ ]
Sun butters pavements. [ ]
Children gather at bus stops. [ ]
Total [ ]

Uproar! Such joy! [ ]
The net bulges again. [ ]
High fives all round. [ ]
Total [ ]

My ginger cat trots in. [ ]
His side strokes my leg, his hungry [ ]
eyes fix on me. [ ]
Total [ ]

Tenth planet beyond [ ]
tiny Pluto, waiting to be found [ ]
in another millennium. [ ]
Total [ ]

Make up a haiku about a planet, using the information you collected for the other activity sheet. Try to make sure that you have exactly 17 syllables.

ideas page

School

Introduction

This exercise encourages children to examine their feelings about school, and to write about them clearly and vividly. While it is important to foster a generally positive view of school, likes and dislikes are a normal part of the human experience; by channelling their feelings into poetry, the children will produce something positive and will benefit from sharing ideas. The children will also be looking at verse structure and using metaphors and similes.

Learning Objectives

- To write clear, vivid poems based on their feelings about school.
- To examine verse structure.
- To use metaphors and similes.

Discussion

Ask the children to read *What I like about school*. This is based on Edwin Morgan's *A view of things* in his *Collected Poems*, published by Carcanet Press, and follows a distinct pattern. Help the children to identify this pattern. It would be helpful to read the poems aloud in different ways; for example, the whole class could read out 'What I like/hate about school', and individual children could take turns at responding with the rest of the sentence. The children could incorporate a range of voices and expressions, and generally have fun with the poem.

Activity Pages

Love it or loathe it?
Ask the children to close their eyes and think about all the different parts of the school, from the headteacher's room to the farthest end of the field. Collect words from the children about school and put some of them on a flipchart or on the board. Ask them what they feel about each part of the school. Try the same exercise, this time with the children keeping their eyes open, and collect more words from them. Then begin the activity.

When the children have completed this activity, ask them to share their responses with the rest of the class. Highlight any similarities in their responses. Discuss ways the children could express their ideas using metaphors or similes, such as 'At playtime the playground swarms like an ant hill.'

Fighting!
Begin by suggesting that one thing no one likes about school is a fight. Then read the poem. Emphasise that the children should use the present tense.

- It will give the children the opportunity to use a tense they rarely use in written work.
- It will make their writing more vivid and immediate.

Ask the children why they think the odd-numbered lines are longer than the even-numbered lines and what effect this has on the structure of the poem. When the children have written their poems, it would be a good opportunity to have a discussion on alternatives to fighting, such as talking over the problem, either with each other or an adult.

Written Work

What I like about school
This idea can be extended to other topics, such as football, tests, music – even 'What I like/dislike about the Vikings' and so on. Invite suggestions for other topics and ask the children to write their feelings up as poems.

The fight
After the children have written their poem about a fight, ask them to think about how it feels to make up after a fight or an argument. Then ask them to write a poem on this topic, again using the present tense.

School

Poetry page

What I like about school

What I like about school is its playtime.
What I hate about school is its injuries at playtime.
What I hate about school is its smell of the toilets.
What I love about assembly is Mr Burley's stories.
What I hate about assembly is my aching legs.
What I love about smells in school is Mrs Ashby's cooking.
What I hate about smells in school is I can't smell the
  cooking smell from the mobile.
What I hate about playtimes is the muddle in the cloakroom.
What I hate about school is being bullied.
What I love about school is getting knowledge about
  Ancient Egypt and electricity.

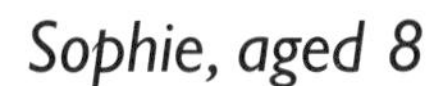

Sophie, aged 8

The fight

There's a fight in the playground today.
  Two big boys from Mr Magee's
Are knocking the daylights out of each other
  Under the trees.

The girls are silent and staring
  And Clare whispers 'Stop it, Paul,'
As the fighting gets wilder and feet jab out
  And fingers maul.

I watch, and I'm glad it's not Joe
  And me in that horrible space –
Not my stomach winded, not my nose bleeding,
  Not my burning face.

The sky is bright. Two planes fly
  Out from the base, while one
Boy holds the other down with his knee
  And breathes 'You done?'

There's a fight in the playground today.
  Paul Topple from Mr Magee's
Is crushing the daylights out of John Randall
  Under the trees.

Fred Sedgwick

Love it or loathe it?

Read *What I like about school* on the poetry page.

1. Now write down six ideas under the headings below. Think about the whole school: playground, classrooms – even the toilets!

What I like about school	What I don't like about school
1. ______	1. ______
2. ______	2. ______
3. ______	3. ______
4. ______	4. ______
5. ______	5. ______
6. ______	6. ______

2. Look at the poem again. It is not just about the school itself. It is about things that happen in school, such as assemblies, or things connected with school, such as smells. On a separate sheet add some more ideas to your list about events or feelings connected with school.

Write your poem. Include things you like and don't like, perhaps on alternate lines; or write two separate poems.

Fighting!

Read *The fight* on the poetry page. Try to imagine how the fighters and the watchers feel.

In the spaces below, describe an imaginary fight as if it is really happening now.

- Imagine how hands and feet feel in a fight.
- Think about the smells of the grass, or the playground or the floor.
- Imagine the voices and other noises going on all around.

There is a fight in our classroom right now

I can see ______________________________

____

____

They are fighting about ______________________________

____

____

They sound like ______________________________

____

____

They look like ______________________________

____

____

I feel ______________________________

____

____

Use your ideas to write a poem about a fight. Imagine it is happening now, and write 'There is'.

ideas page

Animals

Introduction

This exercise will encourage children to look more closely at the behaviour of familiar animals and the way they perceive them. It also explains the concept of cumulative poems. Many of them will be familiar with the format from nursery songs and rhymes, but here they will learn a little more detail about their structure. The children will then use their detailed observations about an animal to write their own cumulative poem.

Learning Objectives

- To examine in detail the behaviour of familiar animals.
- To write a cumulative poem using repeated words.

Discussion

- Read the poem aloud with the children. Then read it out to the class, missing out words for them to call out. You could make it more fun for the children by, for example, beginning the poem in a whisper and growing progressively louder, or even by 'mewing' the poem in a cat-like voice!
- Discuss the nature of a cumulative poem and give some other examples, such as *One man went to mow* or *The house that Jack built.* You may find it helpful to read *The Oxford Nursery Rhyme Book*, edited by Iona and Peter Opie, for more examples. Divide the children into pairs. Give them an animal to work on and ask them to think of as many of its activities as possible. Then ask them to work out how the activities might fit into a cumulative poem. Start them off with an example:
  - My dog shakes water on to everyone when he has been swimming.
  - My dog shakes water on to everyone when he has been swimming and runs among the picnic things.

Activity Pages

Pet pandemonium
The children could first read the poem in pairs, reading it in different ways and allocating parts. The activity prompts the children to think about the different sounds animals make, and then about animal behaviour.

The imaginary cat
For this activity, ask the children to close their eyes while they visualise the imaginary cat. You could encourage the children to play out cat-like activities, such as yawning, grooming themselves and so on. Ask the children to think of words to describe these activities. Use questions such as 'What does the cat remind you of?' 'What does the cat's fur feel like against your leg?' Encourage the children to use similes, reminding them what similes are. Before they tackle the sheet on their own, ask them to write down five phrases beginning with the following:

- *The cat's fur feels as smooth as...*
- *The cat's claws feel as sharp as...*
- *The cat's paw feels as firm as...*
- *The cat's whiskers feel as gentle as...*
- *The cat's ears feel as delicate as...*

Written Work

- When the children have completed the activity pages, ask them to write a cumulative poem about an animal using the observations they have listed. Ask them to focus carefully on the animal's behaviour. What is the animal like in certain positions? What does it smell like or sound like?
- Then ask the children to write a poem about a different animal, using all of their five senses to describe the animal: sight, touch, taste, sound and smell. Explain how taste can be sensed through smell and vice versa – the children should not be attempting literally to taste their pets!
- Ask the children to picture an imaginary animal. Encourage them to be as creative as possible, but at the same time to pay attention to detail, just as they did with the real animals they have been thinking about. They should think about size, shape, texture of skin or fur, physical characteristics such as the way the animal walks (or slithers, swims or crawls!), the sounds it makes and what it eats.

Animals

Poetry page

I am the cat from down the road

I am the cat from down the road.

I am the cat from down the road
(neighbours call me James).

I am the cat from down the road
(neighbours call me James),
and I've adopted all of you,
from twenty-one to eighty-two,
to give me milk, and comfort, too.

I am the cat from down the road
(neighbours call me James),
and I've adopted all of you,
from twenty-one to eighty-two,
to give me milk, and comfort, too.
Stroke me, call me pleasant names.

I am the cat from down the road
(neighbours call me James),
and I've adopted all of you,
from twenty-one to eighty-two,
to give me milk, and comfort, too.
Stroke me, call me pleasant names.
When your front door opens, I'm
always inside in record time.

I am the cat from down the road
(neighbours call me James),
and I've adopted all of you,
from twenty-one to eighty-two,
to give me milk, and comfort, too.
Stroke me, call me pleasant names.
When your front door opens, I'm
always inside in record time.
I mew and moan till the saucer comes.

I am the cat from down the road
(neighbours call me James),
and I've adopted all of you,
from twenty-one to eighty-two,
to give me milk, and comfort, too.
Stroke me, call me pleasant names.
When your front door opens, I'm
always inside in record time.
I mew and moan till the saucer comes.
I lap and stretch by the flicking flames.

I am the cat from down the road.

Fred Sedgwick

Pet pandemonium

Read *I am the cat from down the road* on the poetry page.

1. What sound does the cat make? What other words do we sometimes use to describe this sound? Write down as many as you can think of in the space below.

2. Here are some sentences about animals. Match the sentence with the animal. Write the number of the animal in the box. The first one has been done for you.

I yap at strangers.	3	I squawk to my friends in the sky.		I neigh as I gallop over the fields.	
I hiss to warn you away.		I squeak as I hide in my hole.		I bleat at the sheep-dog.	

Choose two of these animals and write five more lines to describe what each one does. Remember to write as if you were the animal. Think about what you would do if you were them.

The imaginary cat

1. Use your imagination to picture a cat in your head. Then complete these sentences.

As the cat runs to catch a bird it looks like

____

____

As the cat scurries up a tree it looks like

____

____

As the cat is curled up by the fire it looks like

____

____

2. Imagine you are stroking the cat. Think about how its fur feels. Then complete these sentences.

The cat's head feels like

____

____

The cat's ears feel like

____

____

The cat's whiskers feel like

____

____

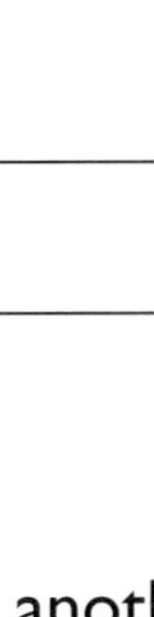

NOW Do the same thing on another sheet for a dog. Use the words 'as' or 'like' to create lots of similes.

Similes use 'like' or 'as' to describe something. 'The cat is as black as night' is a simile.

ideas page

Parents

Introduction

This exercise will help the children to express how they feel about their parents or carers, both when the children are angry and when they are happy. The children will look at the causes of anger and the way anger makes them feel, physically and emotionally. They will also learn how we can associate particular things (in this case, food) with particular people and how these associations can be a source of happy memories.

Learning Objectives

- To express feelings about parents and carers.
- To write poems that express these feelings.

Discussion

- Read *When I was angry* with the class. Ask questions which prompt the children to examine their own feelings when they are angry, such as 'What kinds of things make you feel angry?' 'How do you feel physically when you are angry?' 'Do you see any shapes or colours inside your head when you are angry?' Emphasise that, although anger is powerful at the time, it does pass. Ask how they feel after they have been angry, and how they feel when they are reconciled with their parent.
- Read *To my mum* with the class. Ask them to think of other expressions of incompleteness, such as 'Batman without Robin' or 'Aladdin without his lamp'. Then ask the children to close their eyes and think of things they associate with their parents, grandparents or other loved ones: their clothes, their favourite food, their hobbies, books or newspapers, and anything else that comes to mind. Encourage them to examine how these associations work; for example, 'Grandad's cap on a hook reminds me of walks I've taken with him.'

Activity Pages

Family feuds and fun
Here the children are asked to think about times when they have been happy, and times when they have been angry. All the children will have had good and bad times with their parents or carers, and it is important to deal with this area sensitively, acknowledging that we all feel angry with our loved ones at times while focusing on the positive elements of the relationship.

Food, glorious food!
This activity involves listing favourite foods, activities and places of a parent or carer, reinforcing how certain things can remind us of loved ones.

Written Work

- The lists resulting from each activity sheet could be turned into list poems, with titles such as *Things that make me angry/happy* or *My mother's favourite things*.
- The children could write a story about a funny thing that a parent has done, or a story of a particularly happy day they had with a parent or carer. They could then turn the story, or part of it, into a poem.
- Ask the children to bring in photographs featuring their parents or carers, grandparents or other relatives when they themselves were children. Bring in some old pictures of your own, from books or newspapers, for those children who may not have family photos. Then ask the children to make notes about their photograph, using these questions as prompts:
  - Who might have taken this picture?
  - Describe the expressions on everyone's faces.
  - What might have happened immediately before this picture was taken?
  - What might have happened immediately afterwards?
  - Describe the background to the photograph.
  - What sounds might we hear if this photograph had a soundtrack?

  Then ask the children to make their notes into a poem about the scene.
- Do a similar exercise with the children bringing in photos in which they themselves appear; holiday photographs or pictures of family celebrations such as christenings, bar mitzvahs and so on would be ideal.

Parents

Poetry page

When I was angry

When I was angry
I screamed at my mummy.

Then I was quiet
for a long, long time.

I curled up
in her arms

and said 'Sorry,'
and she said

'That's all right,
My little Chickadee,'

and then she tickled me.

Fred Sedgwick

To my mum

You are
the ketchup
on my chips.
Without you,
I'd be pizza without cheese,
and like a sausage roll
with no sausage.
When you're away
I feel tasteless
and like unfizzy
lemonade.
You are like a peach.
Your taste carries on,
but you never
hit a stone.

Anonymous, aged 8

Family feuds and fun

Read *When I was angry* on the poetry page.

1. Think about times when you have been angry with your parents or whoever looks after you. On a separate sheet, write a few sentences describing a time you were angry and how it felt.

2. Now think about a time when you were happy with that person. Use those memories to help you complete the sentences below.

When I am happy I ______________________________

When I am happy we ______________________________

When I am happy I like to ______________________________

At the end of a happy day I feel ______________________________

Inside my heart I feel ______________________________

Read this sentence about someone's idea of happiness:

Happiness is jazz music and my best friend on a summer night.

Using your own ideas of feelings, finish these sentences:

Happiness is ______________________________

Anger is ______________________________

Sadness is ______________________________

Fear is ______________________________

Food, glorious food!

Think about your parents or someone else who looks after you. Now think of food!

1. Make a list of things your chosen person likes best.

My ____________________ likes

____

____

____

____

____

____

____

____

2. Next, make a list of pastimes or hobbies that your chosen person enjoys.

My ____________________ enjoys

____

____

____

____

____

____

____

____

Think of a place your person likes to go, and write down three reasons why they like it. For example: my Dad likes the seaside because he likes to swim in the sea, he likes to eat ice-cream on the beach and he likes the amusement arcades.

ideas page

Siblings

Introduction

This section focuses on sibling relationships. It would be useful to ask the children to bring in pictures of babies, ideally photographs of themselves as babies, or else pictures taken from magazines. These could be displayed and used as prompts for the 'Babies' activity page. They could also bring in photos of their siblings to make a 'brothers and sisters' display board.

Learning Objectives

- To reflect on family relationships.
- To understand how particular things can remind them of particular people.
- To write about family members using similes and metaphors.

Discussion

- When discussing the poem *Brother, sister and baby*, point out how the narrator recalls her siblings by thinking about things she associates with them. Invite the children to talk about their own siblings (or cousins or friends, if they have none). Ask them what kinds of things remind them of their siblings.
- When discussing *My baby has a neck in creases*, emphasise how even a short poem can contain a wealth of close observations. Using pictures of babies as prompts, invite suggestions on ways to describe the different parts of babies. Encourage imaginative use of metaphors and write any good suggestions on the board.
- If it is feasible, try to arrange for a baby to be brought into the classroom and washed, fed and changed by one of its parents. This would be a valuable experience for those children who do not have babies in their families.
- Afterwards, the children could be asked to draw the baby, concentrating on details such as eyes, skin creases, toes, fingernails and so on. The children could also make notes as the basis for a poem called *Baby crying, Baby being bathed* or *Baby feeding*. Encourage the children to look and listen very carefully and, if appropriate, smell and touch.

Activity Pages

Brothers and sisters

Encourage the children to develop their lists by adding details. For example, instead of writing 'teddy', they could expand this to 'the blue teddy my sister got from Grandma at Christmas'; 'the football boots my brother wore when his school team won the cup'.

Babies

The children are being asked to focus on the physical characteristics of babies. Encourage them to avoid clichés such as 'cute'; instead, help them to enrich their lists by using imaginative metaphors: 'The baby's tummy is soft but firm, like a bouncy castle.'

Written Work

- The children are asked to write a poem about a sister or brother using all the data they have collected.
- They are also asked to write a poem about a baby. They should write about all five senses in their poem, so go over them: sight, touch, taste, smell and hearing. Ask the class for a list of baby noises, and for different ways to describe the noises, such as gurgling, laughing and so on. Try to help them avoid sentimental words and to be realistic in their descriptions.
- The children could mount their poems afterwards and display them next to the pictures of the babies and their brothers and sisters.
- Ask the children to write a poem called *My big sister's/ brother's bedroom*, 'dishing the dirt' on what goes on between siblings. Prompt them to write about the good and bad sides of having brothers and sisters.
- Ask them to write a poem called *Only child*, describing what it is like to be an only child, for example, at bed-time, on holiday or other family occasions. Prompt them to write about the good and bad sides of being an only child.

Siblings

Poetry page

Brother, sister and baby

When I see
dirty socks
thrown in a corner
like some dead creature
that I've never heard of,
I think of my big brother.

When I see
CDs and bright clothes
all over the floor
like things bought at a fairground,
I think of my big sister.

When I see
a chewed dummy
and jam on a pink face,
I think of our baby.

When I think of kindness
I think of
my big brother,
my big sister
and our baby,

and our baby looking up
to kiss me,
all red.

Emily Roeves

My baby has a neck in creases

My baby has a mottled fist,
  My baby has a neck in creases;
My baby kisses and is kissed,
  For he's the very thing for kisses.

Christina Rossetti, 1830–1894

Brothers and sisters

Read the poem *Brother, sister and baby* on the poetry page. Then think of some things that remind you of your own brothers and sisters. (If you don't have any, think of a friend, cousin or neighbour.)

1. Choose one person to write about. Make a list of things that remind you of that person, such as seeing their toys on the floor, or hearing the theme tune of their favourite television programme.

2. Now write a short paragraph about your chosen person. Describe the way they look, mention things they like to do or the way they behave.
   Example: 'My brother always curls up into a ball on the sofa to watch television.'

Use your notes to write a poem about your person. Remember to include the way they look, the things they like and their habits – even annoying ones! Try to include something that makes this person *them*, different from everyone else.

Babies

Read *My baby has a neck in creases* on the poetry page.

1. Think about the different parts of a baby's body. In the space below, write a line describing what each bit looks like. The first one is done for you.

The baby's toes are like tiny baked beans.
The baby's eyes are like
The baby's feet are like
The baby's neck is like
The baby's tummy is like
The baby's hands are like

2. Christina Rossetti uses words like 'creases' and 'dimpled' in her poem to help us picture the baby. Here is a list of words that could be used in a poem about a baby. Add some words of your own.

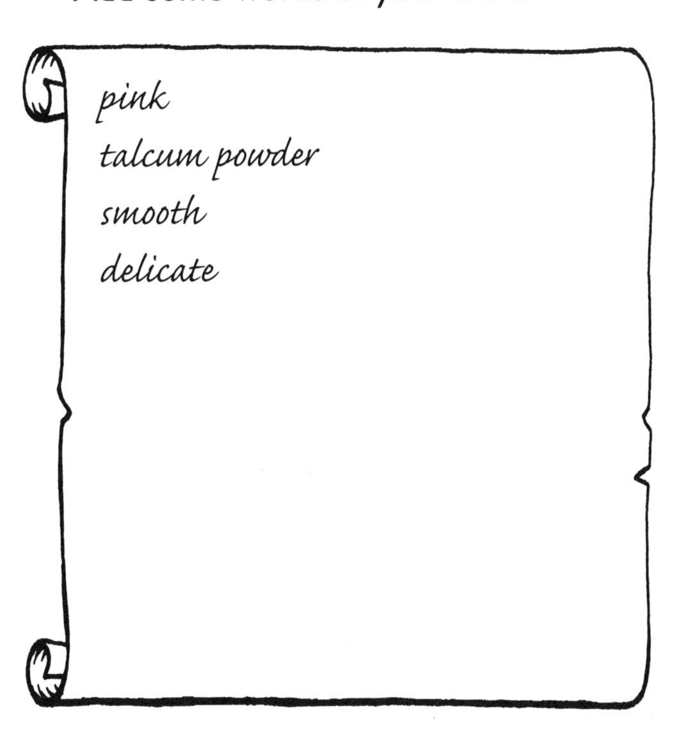

Write a poem about a baby. Use some of the similes you made up earlier to make the reader really see the baby. Describe how the baby sounds and how it smells. Be realistic – remember things like smelly nappies!

ideas page

Feelings

Introduction

This exercise helps the children to explore anger and sulkiness in a positive way, accepting that everyone feels like this at some stage. They will analyse different expressions of these emotions, and compare the differences between feeling angry and happy.

By drawing each other's angry and happy faces, they will examine the physiological changes wrought by different emotions, and will write a poem recalling a time when they were angry or sulky.

Learning Objectives

- To explore their feelings of anger and sulkiness.
- To express their feelings through writing poems.
- To consider the different ways in which we express anger or sulkiness.

Discussion

- Discuss negative feelings in general, such as sulking, dislike, annoyance, even hatred, but especially anger and sulkiness. Explain that everyone feels angry or sulky sometimes, but that these feelings do pass. Invite the children to discuss the things that make them angry or sulky, and how they feel when they are in those states.
- Ask them to make a face showing either anger or sulkiness, and see if the rest of the class can guess which emotion they are displaying. Can they differentiate between an angry face and a sulky one? Ask them to define anger and sulkiness. What makes these feelings go away?
- Using a thesaurus, ask the children to make a list of 'feeling' words. They could turn to the 'angry' section to find out what other words are relevant to anger; then they could do the same with 'sulky', 'cheerful' and 'thoughtful'.

Activity Pages

Feeling angry

The children are asked to draw a picture of their friend's angry face. Encourage them to observe the face they are drawing in minute detail. As the drawings near completion, ask them to write some descriptive words and phrases on the page, such as 'Angry teeth are sharp as nails.' Arrange all the drawings together and read out the phrases to the whole class, emphasising the most unusual. Highlight any similarities or differences in the angry expressions; then repeat the exercise with a cheerful face.

Feeling sulky

When the children have identified the sulky words, point out that there are often many different ways of saying something. Encourage them to think of as many words as possible to use in their poem, and suggest they use a thesaurus. Explore any dialect words they use, such as 'mardy' for 'sulky' (a Lincolnshire word). Using ideas from the poems they write, compose a class poem on feeling sulky; then repeat the exercise with happy feelings.

Written Work

- Ask the children to write a poem beginning 'When I am angry'. The poem should honestly describe what they feel, emotionally and physically, when they are angry. Ask them to use their synonyms for angry.
- As well as writing a poem on feeling angry and sulky, ask the children to write a poem beginning 'When I am happy'.
- Ask the children to write a poem which includes the following lines:
  When I am thoughtful, I...
  When I am confused, I...
  When I am sleepy, I...
  When I am excited, I...
- The poems should contain notes about colour: 'When I am excited, I am red and orange mixing together...'; and actions: 'When I am thoughtful, I curl up in my favourite chair...'

ICT

The children's poems could be displayed alongside photographs of each child expressing the relevant emotions. You could use a digital camera and scanner, if these are available.

Feelings

Poetry page

Being angry

When I was angry
I screamed and I
stamped my feet
and I scribbled
on the walls.
I was quiet for
a long time.
I said sorry
that was all
right then
it was all
back
together
again
the end.

Jenny, aged 5

Kelly Jane alone

In faded jeans
and anorak
I walk along
the railway track.

Disused for more than
twenty years,
it calms my thunder-
storm of tears.

The rails are going
who knows where,
and I'd go too,
but I don't dare.

The voices raised
in disarray
are long ago
and far away.

Wild flowers wave
like tiny flags,
and there's a thrush
that drags and drags

a worm from deep
inside the grass.
The clouds are calm
and small, and cross

the sky beyond
the pylon there...
and I'd go too,
but I don't dare.

The argument
that drove me from
the living room
dies and is gone.

In faded jeans
and anorak
I walk along
the railway track.

Fred Sedgwick

Feeling angry

Read *Being angry* on the poetry page.

1. There are lots of different words for 'angry'. Words with similar meanings are called synonyms. Here are three synonyms for angry. Match the word to the face.

irritated **furious** **cross**

2. Use a thesaurus to find at least three more synonyms for angry.

____

3. Think about times when you felt angry. Then complete these sentences.

I was irritated when ______________________________

I was furious when ______________________________

I was cross when ______________________________

4. Complete these sentences.

When I am angry I______________________________

My body feels ______________________________

My face looks ______________________________

In pairs, make an angry face. On a separate sheet draw a picture of each other's angry face, and write some words underneath describing what the angry face looks like.

Feeling sulky

Read *Kelly Jane alone* on the poetry page.

1. Look at the words in the list below. Choose the ones that have a similar meaning to **sulking** and write them in the space below.

moody	moping
squeamish	huffy
peevish	skulking
hindering	obliging
brooding	grumpy

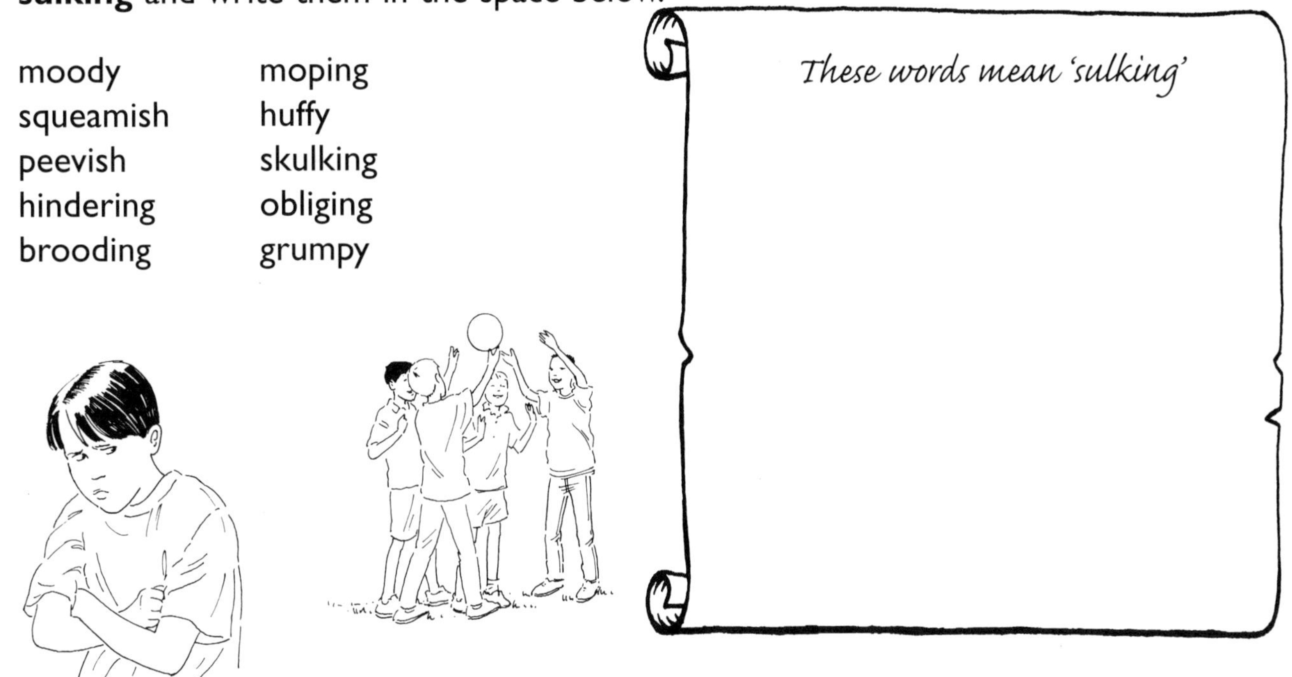

2. Think about a time when you were sulking, then answer these questions.

How did you feel? ______________________________

____

What did you do? ______________________________

____

What did people say to you? ______________________________

____

Write your own poem about how it feels when you are sulking. Does the world look or feel the same as when you are happy? How is it different? You could use some of the words with a similar meaning to sulking. Compare your poem with a friend's. Do you both sulk in the same way?

ideas page

Viewpoints

Introduction

This exercise is designed to help the children explore the rich variety of ways we have of describing things, even everyday, familiar objects, to produce interesting, lively writing. They will be using metaphors, and they will learn to view things from different perspectives, both literally and imaginatively.

Learning Objectives

- To use metaphors.
- To appreciate different ways of looking at things.

Discussion

- Read the poems through with the class, explaining that they are about different ways of looking at things. As an example, hold up a globe and ask for ideas on how to describe it. If necessary, start them off: it is a rounded map; a little world; a sphere. Point out that appearances vary with circumstances. A lamp lit at noon is insignificant, while the same object at night shines like a beacon.
- Do this with as many everyday objects as possible:
  - in the classroom: desks, door handle, computer
  - in the kitchen: saucepan, kettle, taps, sink
  - in the living room: armchair, television, radio, coffee table
  - in an office: filing cabinet, printer
  - in the park: slide, roundabout, climbing frame.
- Make sure that the children are aware that appearances vary with the circumstances and depend upon the position from which a particular object is observed.

Activity Pages

What's your view?
This sheet asks the children to examine a picture of a beach scene and use a wide variety of metaphors to describe what they see in an unusual way. They are then asked to incorporate the metaphors into a poem. Before they begin, divide the class into pairs. Each child then takes turns to say 'From where I am' and the other child completes the sentence, such as: 'the lightbulb is like a bright pear.' They can include objects outside the classroom: 'From where I stand, the town lights are like a necklace strung against the sky.' (This session could be expanded into a performance for an assembly.) Then begin the activity.

Ways of looking
Here the children are given some examples of metaphors. They then have to practise using metaphors correctly, before being asked to make up some of their own. The emphasis is on viewing things in an unusual and different way. Before you begin, give an example of a metaphor and invite ideas. For example, 'the sun breaks through the clouds like a spear' and so on. Then begin the activity. The idea for this activity comes from Wallace Stevens' *Thirteen ways of looking at a blackbird* (*Selected Poems*, Faber and Faber, 1965), and is developed by Sandy Brownjohn in *Does it Have to Rhyme?* (Hodder, 1980). Encourage the children to look at things in as many ways as possible. Rain, for example, is 'a game-destroyer but it helps the crops grow. It is also tears on a classroom window and a chill down the back of my neck. It is pools of black on paving stones, and spears hammering on the road and bouncing off in smashed shards.' They could also describe the sun, wind, hail and snow. Although the children are only asked for one metaphor for the words on the list, ask them to think of several ideas before deciding on the best one.

Written Work

- Expand on the written work in 'What's your view?' by asking the children to write a poem from the viewpoint of an animal; for example, 'From where the cat is, the moon is a saucer of milk far out of reach.'
- The children could use their ideas from 'Ways of looking' to write a poem called *Four ways of looking at ...*, about something they have not yet described. This theme could also be extended to other topics from science or history projects, such as *Four ways of looking at Henry VIII* or *Four ways of looking at electricity*.

Viewpoints

Poetry page

From where I am

From where I am
I can see a night
like a forest
lit by geometric windows.

From where I am
the cat is a shell
curved on the mat
in front of the fire,
and the fire flickers with warmth and thoughts.

From where I am
dinner is a memory
of smells and tastes.

From where I am
my mother sits
watching television,
and suddenly smiles at me.

Emily Roeves

Four ways of looking at a garden

It is my mother's hobby.
I can see her
bending over the herbs.

It is a flag-festival of colour:
red and yellow and green and purple.

It is my brother's goal area:
look at the grass worn away
by his dives.

It is a memory of last summer's barbecue,
the smells of burning burgers.

Emily Roeves

What's your view?

Read *From where I am* on the poetry page. Then look closely at the picture below. You have probably seen all of these things before, but can you think of any unusual ways to describe them? Jot down your ideas in the space below. An example is given for you.

The deck-chair is a striped stick of seaside rock.

Use your ideas to write a poem about the beach. Begin each verse with 'From where I am'. Try to find the most interesting and unusual ways you can think of to describe the items you write about.

Ways of looking

Read *Four ways of looking at a garden* on the poetry page. You will see that there is always more than one way to describe something. For example, you could describe a car as:

- a joyride
- a little room on wheels
- a death-dealer.

These are all **metaphors** for a car. A metaphor is a way of describing something by saying it is like something else.

Here are some more metaphors. Can you match them to the right pictures?

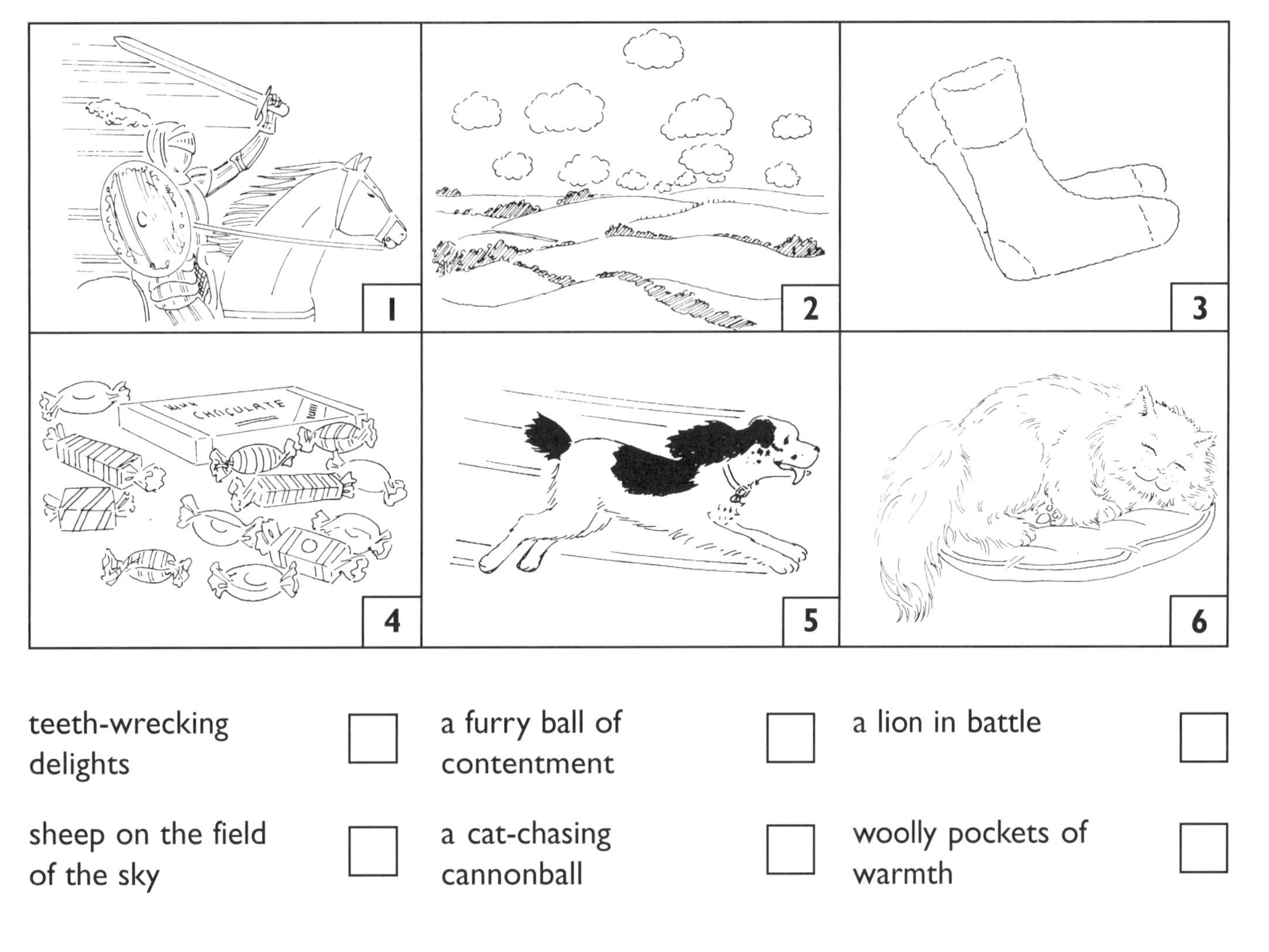

teeth-wrecking delights	☐	a furry ball of contentment	☐	a lion in battle	☐
sheep on the field of the sky	☐	a cat-chasing cannonball	☐	woolly pockets of warmth	☐

Think of a metaphor for these:

ideas page

Holidays!

Introduction

This exercise introduces children to two relatively sophisticated elements of poetry: alliteration and onomatopoeia. The long names may seem a little daunting, so it is important to explain their meanings clearly and, above all, to encourage the children to see that they can have great fun using these features in their writing, or even in their speech. The children will also be thinking once again of how different senses can be stimulated by different experiences and sensations, in the context of happy, fun days out. This lesson would be particularly appropriate for the summer months.

Learning Objectives

- To introduce children to alliteration.
- To introduce children to onomatopoeia.
- To think about the freedom of holiday times and how holidays appeal to the senses.

Discussion

- Read the poems with the class. Discuss with the children which poems they prefer, and compare their forms, pointing out the differences in verse structure and the use of powerful verbs. Explain the concepts of alliteration and onomatopoeia. You could use a nursery rhyme, such as 'Peter Piper picked a peck of pickled pepper' to illustrate alliteration. Onomatopoeia may sound like a difficult word, but point out the onomatopoeic words in the second poem, such as 'lolling', 'bash', 'belt' and so on to help them understand the concept. Invite suggestions for other words which sound like their meaning; ask someone to yawn whilst saying the word 'yawn' to demonstrate the idea!
- Encourage the children to think about the subject matter of the poems in terms of their five senses. What do they see on a day out? What do they hear, taste, smell and touch? Remind them to think about colour, shape, noise and atmosphere.

Activity Pages

The feel of the fair

Before beginning the activity, have a brainstorming session with the class discussing the five senses and things which appeal to each. Then divide the class into groups of three or four and ask them to talk about fairs. Nominate one person from each group to write down all the words they can think of on what fairs smell, sound, feel, taste and look like. After ten minutes, invite each group to present their words and phrases to the rest of the class.

Summer sights, sounds and smells

Before beginning the activity, ask the children simply to list the things they would do on the first day of the summer holidays. Emphasise that all you are asking for at this stage is a list, not a full-blown poem. Then discuss alliteration and onomatopoeia, and ask them to apply these to their lists. Encourage them to use words which are relevant as well as alliterative or onomatopoeic. The missing words are: splashes; belted or batted; and flickered.

Written Work

- Ask the children to write a poem about a place they would like to visit. Encourage them to use their five senses and to include colour, shape and noise in the poem.
- Ask the children to turn their lists of things to do on the first day of the summer holidays into a poem using alliteration and/or onomatopoeia. Alliteration is the use of repeated consonants; assonance is the use of the same vowel sound with different consonants, or the same consonant with different vowels. If this distinction would be helpful to your class, point it out, but the main objective is to encourage the children to use repeated letters.
- The children could do a similar exercise on 'Things to do on Christmas morning' or 'Things to do on the first day after Ramadan'. Every Saturday is a little holiday for most of us. Ask the children to write a poem about their Saturdays, using these prompts plus any of your own ideas:
  - When I wake up on Saturday I ...
  - When Saturday comes I ...
  - Saturday smells like ...

Holidays!

Poetry page

Tomorrow I'm going to the fair

Tomorrow I'm going to the fair.
The others in our class'll be there,
coins stuffed into anoraks,
crashing around the dodgem tracks.

Tomorrow I'm going to the fair.
Jessica Jackson-Wood will be there
on the Flying Roletto, as high as high,
while her mother squints at the terrible sky.

The boys from Inkerman Street will be in
The Ghost Train making a ghastly din.
They'll suck at candy floss and smoke,
and go home loud and happy and broke.

Tomorrow I'm going to the fair.
There's nothing on earth that can compare
with the raucous light and the flashing sound
as Jessie and I whirl the dodgems around.

Fred Sedgwick

Things to do on the first day of the summer holidays

Lie in bed late, lounging and lolling about.
Eat eggs and bacon for breakfast at eleven.

Sprawl on the lawn with a long glass of lemonade
And eat salad and seafood. Travel the town, tee-shirted.

Greeting mates, grinning with freedom. Bowl.
Bash those bails down. Belt a leather ball

Bouncing to the boundary, bounce, bounce... Bring
a take-away home, parathas and poppadoms.

Talk about treats: sunlight through trees and sand.
Sleep in deep silence between sheets. Dream.

Fred Sedgwick

The feel of the fair

Remember – the five senses are sight, touch, taste, sound and smell.

Read *Tomorrow I'm going to the fair* on the poetry page.

1. Close your eyes and imagine that you are at a fair. Now look at the pictures below. Each of these appeals to a different sense. Some of them appeal to more than one. In the box, write down which sense, or senses, you think the item appeals to most. The first one is done for you.

2. Write down four more things about the fair that you really like. For each one, use a metaphor to describe the way your chosen subject appeals to your senses. An example is done for you.

I like **candy floss** because **it tastes like the summer holidays**.

I like ______________________________ .

I like ______________________________ .

I like ______________________________ .

I like ______________________________ .

Choose one thing that you like best about the fair and write a poem about it.

Summer sights, sounds and smells

Read *Things to do on the first day of the summer holidays* on the poetry page.

1. In each line of this poem there are several words beginning with the same letter. This is called **alliteration**. In the first line it is the letter **l**. Go through the poem and find out which letter is repeated like this in the other lines. Then write down all the words in the line that begin with that letter. The first line has been done for you.

line 1	l	lie, late, lounging, lolling	line 6		
line 2			line 7		
line 3			line 8		
line 4			line 9		
line 5			line 10		

2. In line seven the sound of the words beginning with 'b' is like the sound of a ball bouncing along. When a word sounds like the thing it means, it is called **onomatopoeia**. See if you can finish the words in these sentences. Remember you are looking for words that sound like their meaning!

Water softly | s | p | | | | h | | | into the pool.

Bill | b | | | t | | d | the ball to the boundary.

The flames | | | i | | k | | | | d | in the frosty night.

Write down four lines on things you would like to do on the first day of the summer holidays. Two of the lines should use alliteration, and two should use onomatopoeia. Here are two examples:

Balance beautifully on my bicycle.
Hiss like a snake in my sister's ear!

ideas page

Sports

Introduction

Most children enjoy physical activity, and this exercise gives an opportunity to harness that enthusiasm and apply it to poetry, both by reading about sport and by writing about it. In the process, the children will also learn about kennings, a poetic device traditionally associated with Old English or Norse poetry, but which can still provide a great deal of fun for modern readers and writers.

Learning Objectives

- To introduce children to the concept of kennings in poetry.
- To think about the pleasure of physical activity.
- To convey vigour and movement in their own poetry.

Discussion

- Explain that a kenning is a style of describing something and give some examples: a dog could be a tail-wagger, a breath-monster, a bath-hater or a pond-splasher. Tell the children that they will be making up some kennings of their own.
- Then ask them to imagine they are running a race. Ask them about the different physical sensations they feel before, during and after the race, and write some of their answers on one half of the board. Then get the class to turn their answers into kennings on the other half of the board. For example, if someone has suggested 'panting', write 'panting-maker' (or heart-buster or tape-breaster, depending on their ideas).
- Next, ask the children to imagine that they are: lifting weights; throwing a heavy ball; throwing a discus; throwing a javelin; wrestling a strong opponent to the floor.
- Then ask them to compose a kenning about one of these activities; for example, for throwing a javelin:
  Arm strainer
  Death launcher
  Sharp point deliverer...
- Encourage the children to add to the kennings to make them into more than a list; for example:
  When I throw a javelin
  I am aware
  of an arm strainer in my hand;
  of a death launcher
  if someone
  is in the way;
  A sharp point deliverer
  is at the end
  of my spear.

Activity Pages

A riddle-writer
Read the poem *Goal!* with the class. Then prepare them for the activity sheet by inviting the class to suggest kennings for a particular sporting activity, such as a hole in one in golf, or the dive beginning a swimming race. (The answers to the riddles are: a football net; a cricket wicket; hurdling; and a tennis ace.)

Under the water
This activity is designed to help children use all their senses to describe the feeling of being underwater. Before they begin, ask the children to close their eyes and imagine they are underwater. Ask them what the sights, sounds, smells and so on are like. Then begin the activity. Once the children have identified the different sensations, encourage them to turn them into kennings to write their poem.

Written Work

- Ask the children to develop their ideas to write a kenning about scoring a goal, or winning a race, or any other dramatic highlight of a game or sporting activity, such as winning a championship at Wimbledon.
- Ask the children to write a list poem of all the different experiences they feel as they ride a bike or run through the park: sunshine, the air rushing into their faces and so on. Encourage them to use the word 'like' as often as they can, as in 'It feels like/sounds like/smells like' and so on. Also encourage them to use all their senses.
- Ask the children to write another list poem about a sport they have never taken part in, such as sky-diving or skiing, again using the word 'like' and their five senses. Encourage them to use their imagination as much as possible.

Sports

Poetry page

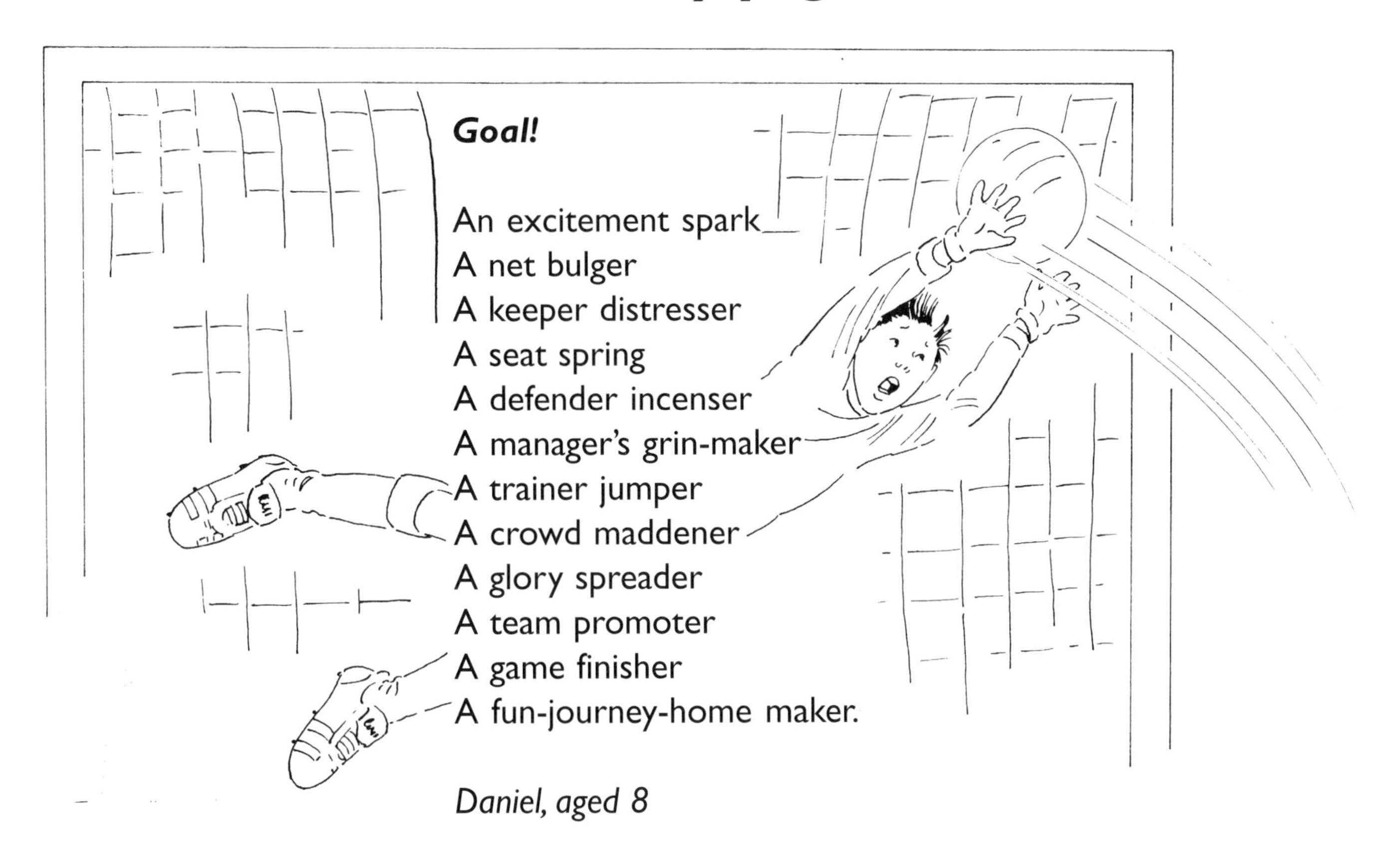

Goal!

An excitement spark
A net bulger
A keeper distresser
A seat spring
A defender incenser
A manager's grin-maker
A trainer jumper
A crowd maddener
A glory spreader
A team promoter
A game finisher
A fun-journey-home maker.

Daniel, aged 8

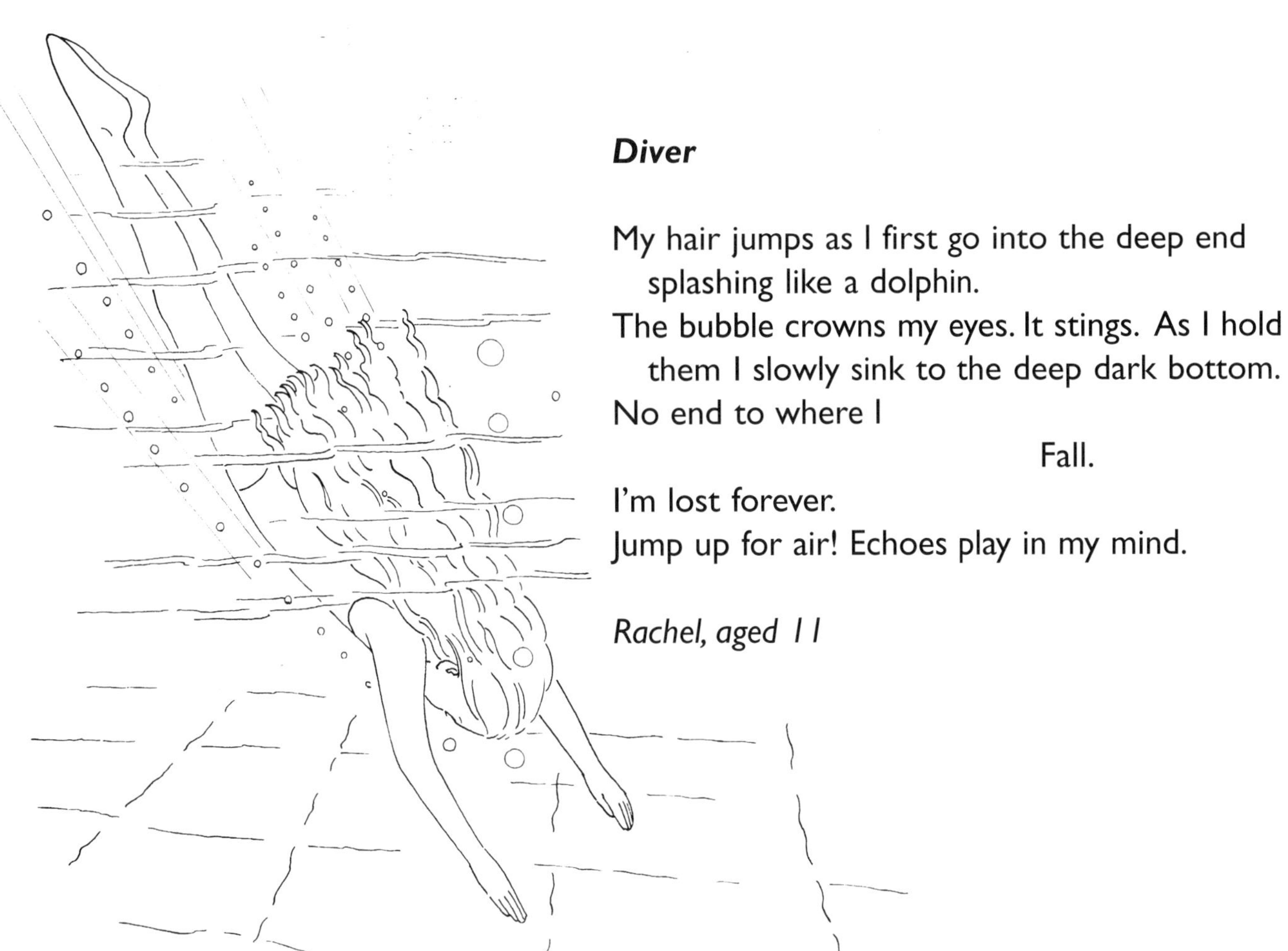

Diver

My hair jumps as I first go into the deep end
splashing like a dolphin.
The bubble crowns my eyes. It stings. As I hold
them I slowly sink to the deep dark bottom.
No end to where I
Fall.
I'm lost forever.
Jump up for air! Echoes play in my mind.

Rachel, aged 11

A riddle-writer

Read *Goal!* on the poetry page. Although Daniel's poem is called *Goal!* he doesn't use that word. Instead, Daniel has written words and phrases describing what a goal is like. This kind of poem is called a **kenning**.

People sometimes make up puzzles or riddles using kennings. The sets of kennings below are about things to do with sport. See if you can work out what they are about, and write your answers in the boxes.

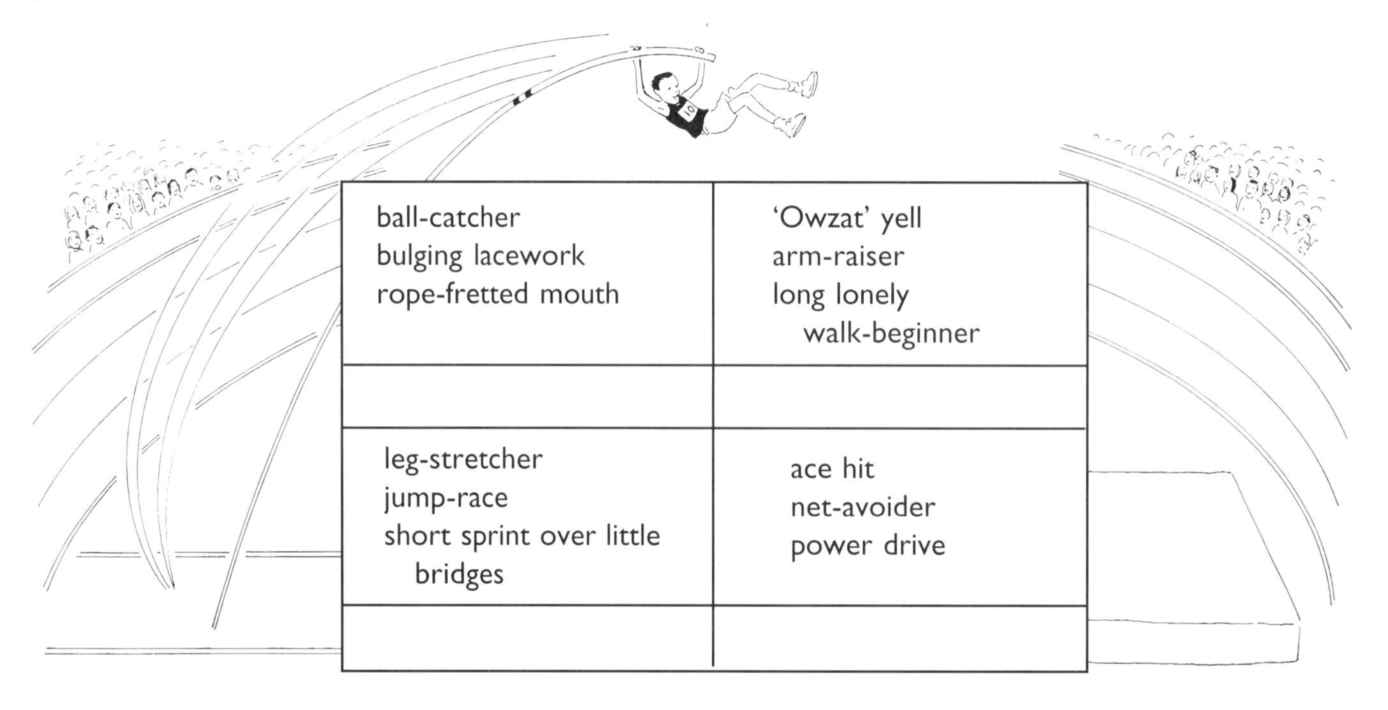

ball-catcher bulging lacework rope-fretted mouth	'Owzat' yell arm-raiser long lonely walk-beginner
leg-stretcher jump-race short sprint over little bridges	ace hit net-avoider power drive

Write a kenning about your favourite sport. Be as inventive as you can. Example:

athletics: a block-shover; a heart-stretcher; a muscle-tester.

Read your poem to a friend. See if you can each work out what the other's poem is about!

A kenning is a way of describing something. 'Sea-stallion' is a kenning for boat.

Under the water

Read *Diver* on the poetry page. Imagine you are swimming underwater. Then fill in your answers to the questions.

What can you hear underwater?

____

What can you smell underwater?

____

What can you taste underwater?

____

How do you feel underwater?

____

____

Use your answers to write a poem about swimming underwater. Try to turn your answers into kennings before you begin.

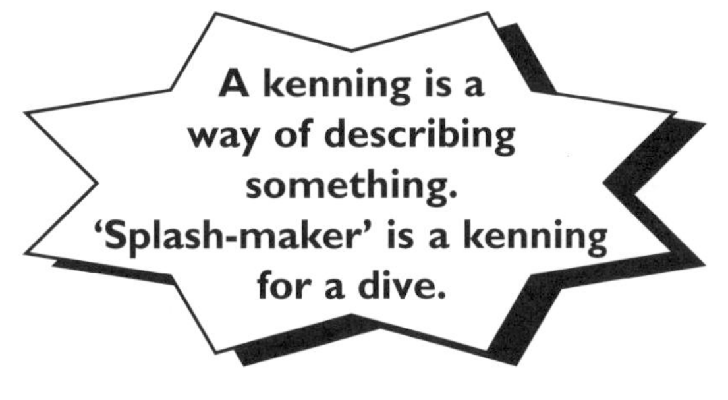

ideas page

Friends

Introduction

This exercise is designed to encourage children to reflect on the nature and meaning of friendship. They will be focusing on the behaviour of friends towards one another, and realising that they can be friends with people outside their own age group, or with people whose tastes differ from their own.

Learning Objectives

- To consider the nature and meaning of friendship.
- To write poems about their friends.

Discussion

- Ask the children to close their eyes and think of all the good things their friends do for them; ask them to come up with at least ten ideas and then invite them to share their thoughts with the rest of the class. Use the material they suggest as the basis for a discussion on friends.
- Some useful prompt questions are:
  - What are friends for?
  - What do friends do for us when we are in trouble?
  - What do they do for us when we are happy?
- Encourage the children to come up with a wide variety of examples, and include practical things, such as 'My friend sends me postcards when she goes away'; 'My friend gives me a present on my birthday'; as well as emotional things such as 'My friend hugs me when I'm feeling sad.' Talk about friendship generally, and why friendships are important to us, focusing on the good things in friendship, such as laughter, shared meals and days out.
- Turn the discussion around and ask the children to think of five things they do for their friends. Use the children's suggestions to extend the talk about the nature of friendship, especially the notions of selfishness and selflessness.

Activity Pages

Things friends do
Here the children are asked to think about the structure of their poems. Encourage them to play with the order of their verses, changing words, making lines shorter or longer and using a thesaurus to help them choose the most powerful words. Have them read their poems aloud to hear how they sound. They could repeat this exercise using a list of things they do for their friends.

Different friends
Before they begin their lists, encourage the children to think of the small details that contribute to a sense of friendship: 'Mrs Brown always smiles at me when she helps me to cross the road.'

Written Work

- Ask the children to picture an imaginary friend they would like to have, perhaps someone with special powers who could share adventures with them, or a fantasy character like a talking dragon. What would they like this friend to do for them? Ask them to make a list poem about this imaginary friend: he takes me on magic carpet rides; she can turn things into chocolate by magic. Use this exercise to examine the difference between fairy-tale romances and the reality of friendships where differences and imperfections are accepted.
- Ask the children if they have, or have ever had, friends they do not see: friends who live far away, secret 'pretend' friends or friends from a religion, such as Buddha, the Prophet or Jesus. Ask them to write a list poem about what these friends do for them. Give them some examples to start them off:
  He teaches me right from wrong.
  She hides from me.
  He jokes with me.
  He made the world for me.
  He died on a cross for me.
- Ask the children to write an acrostic poem, where the first letter of each line spells out the word 'friend'; for example:
  Fiery of temper at times, but
  Ready to comfort when I am sad ...

Friends

Poetry page

My friend

My friend shares tea with me.
My friend shares biscuits and sweets.
My friend shares toys.
My friend shares with me.

My friend plays 'ring-a-ring-a-roses'.
My friend plays 'sticky toffee'.
My friend plays it.
My friend plays with me.

My friend helps me when I trip over.
My friend helps me to get up.
My friend helps me to tidy up.
My friend helps me.

My friend is kind in the swimming pool.
My friend is kind in the playground.
My friend is kind in the classroom.
My friend is kind to me.

Six children, aged 7

I like you even though

I like you
even though
you talk too much about football.

I like you
even though
you wear clothes that are too
bright.

I like you
even though
you didn't ask me to your party two
years ago.

I like you
even though
you support Man United.

I like you
even though
you were unimpressed by my little
garden with its flowers.

Emily Roeves

Things friends do

Read *My friend* on the poetry page.

1. Think about your own friends. What do they do for you? Try to think of some unusual things. Then write 12 of them down in the boxes below. Some examples are done for you.

My friend gives me samosas.	My friend misses me when I am away from school.

2. Cut out your 12 phrases:
   - Arrange them into three groups of four lines.
   - Make each group into a four-line verse, so that you have a poem with three verses.
   - Change the order of the lines until you find the version you like best.
   - Write your poem out on a separate sheet.

Choose just one friend and write a poem about them. Write three verses. Say what your friend has done for you in the past, what they do for you now, and what they will do for you in the future. Then give your poem to your friend.

Different friends

Read *I like you even though* on the poetry page. As you can see, it is possible to be friends with people who are very different from us! They may like different things, or be different ages from us.

Think of four grown-ups who are friends of yours, such as aunts or uncles, neighbours, teachers and so on.

- Choose two of these grown-up friends and write their names in the boxes.
- Write down something each friend has done for you in the past, something they do now, and something they will do in the future.

Example

Mr Mohammed
Mr Mohammed helped me across the road yesterday.
Today he shouted 'Good luck with your maths test!'
Tomorrow he will probably say 'Have a good weekend!'

Think of a friend who is different from you. Make a list of all the things they do or like that you don't like. Then turn your list into a poem, putting 'I like you even though' before each line.

Glossary

acrostic — A poem in which certain letters form a word. Single acrostics are formed by initial letters, double acrostics by initial and final letters, and triple acrostics by initial, middle and final letters.

alliteration — The use of the same consonant at the beginning of each word, as in 'Peter Piper picked a peck of pickled pepper.'

assonance — The use of the same vowel sounds with different consonants, or the same consonants with different vowels; for example, prime and tight or history and hastily.

haiku — A Japanese verse form with 17 syllables, five in the first line, seven in the second and five in the third.

kenning — A metaphoric verse form characteristic of Old Norse and Old English poetry, describing one thing in terms of another, such as 'sea stallion' for 'ship'.

metaphor — A figure of speech implying a comparison between two things where no literal similarity exists; for example, 'the ship ploughs the sea' implies a comparison between a ship and a plough.

onomatopoeia — Words that imitate the sound they describe, such as babble, buzz or hiss.

riddle — A question or verse designed to be a puzzle, requiring some effort to understand its meaning.

simile — A figure of speech expressing the resemblance of one thing to another, usually introduced by 'like' or 'as'.

Useful reading:

Does it Have to Rhyme?, Sandy Brownjohn, (Hodder, 1980).